Introduction

Tackling multiple choice questions

Multiple choice questions form part of the exam for your second unit in the modular GCSE maths specification. This book has plenty of practice questions to help you get used to multiple choice questions and the technique involved. It also has two practice papers laid out like the real exam to get you ready for the big day.

The multiple choice questions in the exam consist of the question, and then five possible answers. Only one of these will be the correct answer but sometimes the other four will have been chosen in such a way that the correct answer is not immediately obvious.

There are some important things to remember about the multiple choice part of your exam

- The exam is half an hour long and has 25 questions, so you have just over a minute for each question.
- This means you do not want to waste a lot of time on one question – if you are unsure about the answer, leave it and come back to it later.
- Do try to answer every question, even if you have to guess, as there is no penalty for marking the wrong answer.
- There will always be only one correct answer, and if you select more than one, you will get no marks for that question.
- You are allowed to change your mind, but because you will not get any marks if more than one answer is picked, make sure that you erase your previous answers. If you are doing an on-screen or Optical Mark Reader (OMR) test, make sure you are familiar with what to do if you wish to change your answer.
- If you are doing the OMR test make sure you have the right type of pencil (HB), a good eraser, and that you fill in the circle completely.

Helpful tips for answering multiple choice questions

- You can break down the sorts of questions you will come across into four types:
  1. Questions you can easily answer
  2. Questions where some of the answers are not sensible
  3. Questions where an estimate will be good enough to identify the correct answer
  4. Questions where you really do not know the answer – these are the ones worth guessing.
- You can often work out which answer is the correct one without actually doing the calculation – you will find in many questions that the sensible choices are limited, and you can improve your chances by ruling out the obviously wrong answers.
- If that doesn't work, try to estimate what the answer would be and look for the answer that is closest to that estimate.

- Answers will not follow a pattern but there are likely to be similar numbers for each letter choice. i.e.there will be about 5 As, 5 Bs etc. This might help you when you have to guess an answer.
- It is unusual for three consecutive answers to be the same.

Each topic has only a limited number of ways of being tested. Make sure you do plenty of multiple choice examples so that you know the various ways a topic can be tested. Also, practice complete tests to get familiar with the timings.

The best method for doing a multiple choice exam is to

- Work through, answering only the questions you are sure about and can do quickly. Make a note of the numbers for the questions that you are leaving for later.
- Now check how much time is left and how many questions need answering

If the test is done on-line, you will need to keep a note of the questions that have been left for later.

Examples

Some questions can be answered by estimating.

1   What is 3.21×9.7?

    A 311.37   **B** 5.136   **C** 30.137   **D** 51.36   **E** 31.137

The answer must be about $3.2 \times 10 = 32$
It must have a total of $2 + 1 = 3$ decimal places.
The last digit must come from 1×7 (the last digits of the numbers).

Hence the answer can only be **C** or **E**.
The estimate of 10 is 0.3 more than 9.7 so 32 is about $0.3 \times 32 = 0.9$, too big.
The answer is **E**.

2   A car driver calculates that she can travel 13.5 miles for every litre of petrol. How many miles can she travel on 38 litres?

    A 513   **B** 148   **C** 2.8   **D** 24.5   **E** 342

This is roughly $10 \times 40 = 400$ so **B**, **C** and **D** must be wrong.
342 is too small as $38 \times 10 = 380$ so the answer must be **A** 513.

3   What is $83.47 - 28.74$?

    A 65.33   **B** 50   **C** 54.73   **D** 6533   **E** 5473

The answer must be about $80 - 30 = 50$.
The answer must end in 3 ($7 - 4 = 3$).
Hence the answer can only be 54.73.
The answer is **C**.

Sometimes you can use the answers.

Here are the first five terms of an arithmetic sequence

5, 9, 13, 17, 21

What is the expression, in terms of n, for the nth term of this sequence?

A n **B** 25   **C** $5n$ **D** $4n + 1$ **E** $\frac{n}{4}$

put $n = 1$ in each answer.

The only one to give the first term of 5 is **D** as $4 \times 1 + 1 = 5$.

1   Work out the area of this shape.

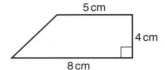

A 26 cm²   **B** 20 cm²   **C** 17 cm²   **D** 40 cm²   **E** 160 cm²

The answer must be smaller than the rectangle 8 cm $\times$ 5 cm $= 40$ cm²
The answer must be larger than the rectangle 5 cm $\times$ 4 cm $= 20$ cm²

The only possible answer is **A** 26 cm²

Sometimes you can use the diagrams.

Some questions often have a diagram. Although these are not accurately drawn they are usually good enough to know if the answer is acute, obtuse or reflex if the question involves an angle.

2

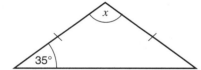

What is the size of the angle marked x in this triangle?

A 35°   **B** 130°   **C** 110°   **D** 70°   **E** 55°

The angle is obviously larger than 90°. Hence **A**, **D** and **F** are not possible.
130° would mean the other two angles add up to 50° (angles in a triangle equal 180°) so **B** is not the answer as the other two angles add up to 70° (isosceles triangle).
This only leaves **C** 110° which is the correct answer.

Published by Edexcel Limited, One90, High Holborn, London, WC1V 7BH

Distributed by Pearson Education Limited, Edinburgh Gate, Harlow, Essex, CM20 2JE, England
www.longman.co.uk

© Keith Pledger, Gareth Cole, Peter Jolly, Graham Newman 2008

The rights of Keith Pledger, Gareth Cole, Peter Jolly and Graham Newman to be identified as the authors of this Work have been asserted by them in accordance with the Copyright, Designs and Patent Act, 1988.

First published 2008
ISBN-13: 978-1-405-88464-8

Typeset by Tech-Set, Gateshead. Printed in the UK.

The publisher's policy is to use paper manufactured from sustainable forests.

6 Introducing number

6.1 Numbers and place value

1 The value of the 6 in the number 3265 is

   A 60

   B 6

   C 600

   D 6000

   E $\frac{6}{10}$

2 The value of the 2 in the number 5219 is

   A 20

   B 2

   C 200

   D 2000

   E $\frac{2}{100}$

3 What is the value of the 7 in the number 7156?

   A 70

   B 7

   C 700

   D 7000

   E $\frac{7}{1000}$

4 The value of the 4 in the number 3214 is

   A 40

   B 4

   C 400

   D 4000

   E $\frac{1}{4}$

5 The number five thousand and eighty seven written in figures is

   A 5870

   B 5087

   C 5078

   D 50 087

   E 50 870

6 Here is a set of 4 cards.
Each card has a number written on it.

Which of these is the largest number that can be made from the 4 cards?

   A 4718

   B 1478

   C 8174

   D 8714

   E 8741

7 Which list of numbers is in order of size?

   A 12   25   37   19   29

   B 19   12   29   25   37

   C 12   19   25   29   37

   D 37   25   29   12   19

   E 29   19   37   25   12

6.2 Number lines

1

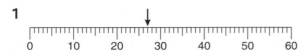

What number does the arrow mark?

A 27

B 20.7

C 2.7

D 33

E 22

2

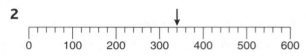

What number does the arrow mark?

A 320

B 32

C 340

D 34

E 460

3

What number does the arrow mark?

A 42

B 40.2

C 40.4

D 44

E 404

4

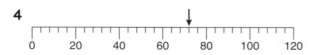

What number does the arrow mark?

A 66

B 72

C 84

D 75

E 70

5

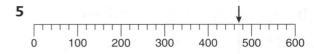

What number does the arrow mark?

A 47

B 407

C 40.7

D 470

E 475

6.3 Rounding numbers

1 What is 5672 when rounded to the nearest 100?

A 57

B 5700

C 56

D 5600

E 6000

2 What is 3493 when rounded to the nearest 1000?

A 4

B 4000

C 3

D 3000

E 3500

3 What is 2965 when rounded to the nearest 10?

A 70

B 2960

C 60

D 3000

E 2970

4 What is 4968 when rounded to the nearest 100?

   A 5000

   B 4000

   C 4900

   D 50

   E 49

6.4 Mental methods

1 Liam spends £3.56.
How much change should he get from £5?

   A £1.56

   B £2.44

   C £1.44

   D £2.56

   E £3.56

2 Ted buys a packet of sweets for £1.75 and a can of cola for 35p.
What is the total cost?

   A £36.75

   B £2.35

   C £2.00

   D £2.20

   E £2.10

3 What is the sum of 56 and 89?

   A 155

   B 145

   C 135

   D 146

   E 33

4 What is the difference between 87 and 143?

   A 64

   B 66

   C 56

   D 54

   E 230

5 What is the cost of 4 tyres at £19.90 each?

   A £79.60

   B £76.60

   C £80.40

   D £79.96

   E £79.40

6.5 Written calculations

1 What is the value of 56 + 172 + 9?

   A 137

   B 237

   C 1622

   D 741

   E 227

2 What is the value of 632 + 4286 + 35 + 8?

   A 22 106

   B 481 421

   C 4841

   D 4961

   E 4951

3 What is the value of 400 − 184?

   A 384

   B 284

   C 216

   D 316

   E 584

4 What is the value of 1326 − 859?

  A 577

  B 533

  C 1533

  D 567

  E 467

5 What is the value of 145 × 6?

  A 870

  B 640

  C 876

  D 890

  E 970

6 What is the value of 386 × 4?

  A 123 224

  B 1224

  C 1544

  D 1524

  E 1584

7 What is the value of 804 ÷ 4?

  A 21

  B 210

  C 200

  D 20

  E 201

8 What is the remainder when 843 is divided by 8?

  A 43

  B 3

  C 7

  D 1

  E 4

9 What is the value of 346 × 54?

  A 1384

  B 3114

  C 17 300

  D 18 684

  E 17 024

10 What is the value of 325 × 23?

  A 7475

  B 975

  C 6500

  D 6415

  E 6475

11 What is the value of 375 ÷ 15?

  A 205

  B 25

  C 20

  D 5

  E 35

12 What is the remainder when 709 is divided by 24?

  A 29

  B 9

  C 13

  D 23

  E 19

6.6 Solving problems without a calculator

1 There are 34 people on a bus when it arrives at a bus stop.
At the bus stop 19 people get off and 12 people get on.

The number of people on the bus as it leaves the bus stop is

A 34

B 7

C 12

D 19

E 27

2 Hajra earned £72 for 12 hours work.

The rate of pay for each hour she works is

A £7.20

B £12

C £60

D £6

E £5

3 A case of wine holds 12 bottles.

The number of bottles of wine in 20 cases is

A 24

B 240

C 8

D 32

E 6

4 365 students go on a school trip.
They all travel by coach.
Each coach carries 54 people.

The number of coaches needed is

A 7

B 6

C 5

D 41

E 13

5 Henri won £5000 on the lottery.
He shared the money equally with his family.

How much did each of the 8 members of the family receive?

A £62.50

B £6.25

C £625

D £600

E £60

6.7 Factors and multiples

1 Which of these numbers is a factor of 12?

A 24

B 36

C 6

D 72

E 144

2 Which of these numbers is a multiple of 24?

A 48

B 12

C 6

D 4

E 10

3 3   4   9   36   72

Which two of the numbers in the list are both factors of 18?

A 36, 72

B 4, 9

C 3, 4

D 3, 9

E 3, 36

4 3   4   9   36   72

Which two of the numbers in the list are both multiples of 12?

A 36, 72

B 4, 9

C 3, 4

D 9, 72

E 3, 36

5 3   4   9   24   36

Which number in the list is a common factor of 12 and 18?

A 4

B 36

C 9

D 3

E 24

6.8 Order of operations

1 What is the value of $3 \times 2 + 5$?

A 21

B 10

C 11

D 25

E 13

2 What is the value of $3 + 2 \times 5$?

A 21

B 10

C 11

D 25

E 13

3 What is the value of $4 \times (5 + 3)$?

A 23

B 32

C 12

D 17

E 36

4 What is the value of $(7 - 3) \times 8$?

A 80

B 12

C 24

D 32

E 36

6.9 Writing a number as a product of its prime factors

1 3   4   6   9   15   19

Which two of these numbers, in the list above, are prime numbers?

A 4 and 9

B 3 and 4

C 3 and 19

D 15 and 19

E 4 and 6

2 31   33   35   37   39

Which two of these numbers, in the list above, are prime numbers?

A 31 and 35

B 33 and 39

C 37 and 39

D 35 and 39

E 31 and 37

3 Which of the following is 72 written as a product of its prime factors?

  A 2 × 36

  B 3 × 24

  C 2 × 3 × 12

  D 2 × 3 × 4 × 3

  E 2 × 2 × 2 × 3 × 3

4 Which of the following is 150 written as a product of its prime factors?

  A 2 × 3 × 5 × 5

  B 3 × 75

  C 3 × 50

  D 2 × 3 × 25

  E 10 × 15

6.10 HCF and LCM

1 What is the lowest common multiple (LCM) of 12 and 21?

  A 3

  B 6

  C 84

  D 168

  E 252

2 What is the lowest common multiple (LCM) of 20 and 45?

  A 5

  B 10

  C 90

  D 120

  E 180

3 What is the highest common factor (HCF) of 24 and 84?

  A 3

  B 12

  C 4

  D 168

  E 336

4 What is the highest common factor (HCF) of 36 and 90?

  A 6

  B 9

  C 18

  D 180

  E 360

5 Eric has two flashing bulbs.
One flashes every 6 seconds and one flashes every 8 seconds.
Both lamps start flashing at the same time.

After how long will the bulbs flash at the same time again?

  A 24 seconds

  B 48 seconds

  C 96 seconds

  D 120 seconds

  E 144 seconds

7 Angles 1

7.1 Fractions of a turn and degrees

1

The number of degrees in this marked angle is

A 180°

B 360°

C $\frac{1}{4}$ turn

D 90°

E 270°

2

The number of degrees in this marked angle is

A 180°

B 360°

C $\frac{1}{2}$ turn

D 90°

E 270°

3

The number of degrees in this marked angle is

A 180°

B 360°

C $\frac{1}{4}$ turn

D 90°

E 270°

4

What is the special name of this marked angle?

A Straight line

B Right angle

C Wrong angle

D Left angle

E $\frac{1}{4}$ turn

5

What is the special name of this marked angle?

A Straight line

B Right angle

C Wrong angle

D Left angle

E $\frac{1}{4}$ turn

7.2 What is an angle?

1

Which of these angles is the same size as angle *x*?

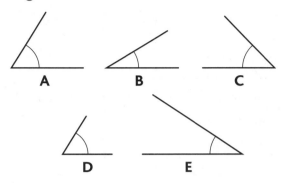

2

The angle between the hands of this clock is

A 90°

B 30°

C 60°

D 45°

E 300°

3

The angle between the hands of this clock is

A 90°

B 30°

C 60°

D 12°

E 240°

4

The angle between the hands of this clock is

A 180°

B 60°

C 120°

D 240°

E 300°

5 Here is a compass.

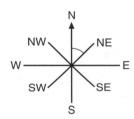

The angle between N and NE is

A 90°

B 180°

C 45°

D 135°

E 315°

6 Here is a compass.

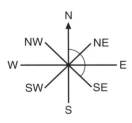

The angle between N and SE is

A 90°

B 180°

C 135°

D 45°

E 225°

7 Here is a compass.

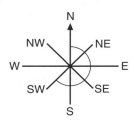

The angle between N and SW is

A   45°

B   225°

C   180°

D   135°

E   270°

7.3 Special types of angles

1 When these angles are arranged in order of size, which angle will be second smallest?

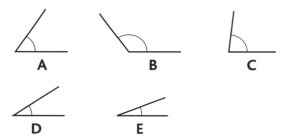

2 If these angles are arranged in order of size, smallest first.

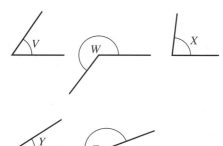

Which of these gives the correct order?

A   YVXWZ

B   VWXYZ

C   ZWXVY

D   VYXWZ

E   ZYVXY

3

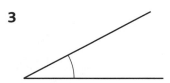

What is the name of this type of angle?

A   Acute

B   Right

C   Obtuse

D   Straight line

E   Reflex

4

What is the name of this type of angle?

A   Acute

B   Right

C   Obtuse

D   Straight line

E   Reflex

5

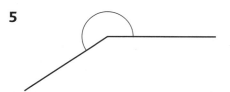

What is the name of this type of angle?

A   Acute

B   Right

C   Obtuse

D   Straight line

E   Reflex

6

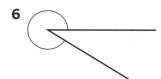

What is the name of this type of angle?

A Acute

B Right

C Obtuse

D Straight line

E Reflex

7.4 Naming sides and angles

1

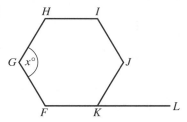

What is the name of the angle marked $x°$?

A Acute

B Angle G

C Reflex

D Angle x

E Angle J

2

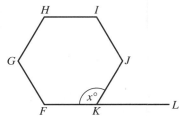

What is the name of the angle marked $x°$?

A Acute

B Angle F

C Reflex

D Angle JKL

E Angle FKJ

3

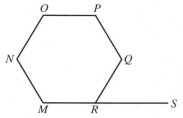

Which line is the longest?

A MR

B MS

C RS

D OP

E QR

4

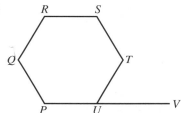

Which angle is the acute angle?

A Acute

B Angle U

C Angle P

D Angle TUV

E Angle PUT

7.5 Perpendicular lines and parallel lines

1

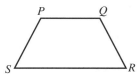

Which two lines are parallel?

A PQ and QR

B PQ and PS

C PQ and SR

D PS and QR

E QR and RS

2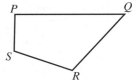

Which two lines are perpendicular?

A PQ and QR

B PQ and PS

C PQ and SR

D PS and QR

E QR and RS

3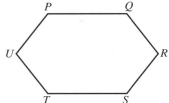

Which two lines are parallel?

A PQ and TS

B PQ and QR

C PU and QR

D UT and RS

E ST and SR

4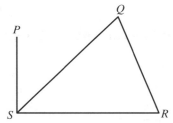

Which two lines are perpendicular?

A PS and QR

B QS and QR

C PS and SR

D PS and QS

E QR and RS

5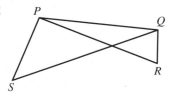

Which line is perpendicular to PS?

A QR

B PR

C QS

D PQ

E SR

6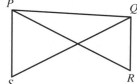

Which line is parallel to PS?

A QR

B PR

C QS

D PQ

E SR

7.6 Estimating angles

1

Without using a protractor, estimate the size of the marked angle.

A 30°

B 60°

C 120°

D 150°

E 45°

2

Without using a protractor, estimate the size of the marked angle.

A 30°

B 60°

C 120°

D 15°

E 45°

3

Without using a protractor, estimate the size of the marked angle.

A 30°

B 60°

C 120°

D 15°

E 45°

4

Without using a protractor, estimate the size of the marked angle.

A 45°

B 60°

C 120°

D 135°

E 225°

5

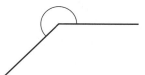

Without using a protractor, estimate the size of the marked angle.

A 45°

B 60°

C 120°

D 135°

E 225°

6

Without using a protractor, estimate the size of the marked angle.

A 30°

B 60°

C 330°

D 300°

E 45°

7.9 Angle facts

1

What is the size of the angle marked $x°$?

A 50°

B 45°

C 40°

D 130°

E 310°

2

What is the size of the angle marked $x°$?

A   35°

B   45°

C   40°

D   125°

E   305°

3

What is the size of the angle marked $x°$?

A   67°

B   57°

C   63°

D   53°

E   143°

4

What is the size of the angle marked $y°$?

A   25°

B   30°

C   290°

D   20°

E   110°

5

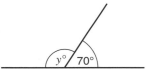

What is the size of the angle marked $y°$?

A   53°

B   57°

C   63°

D   33°

E   237°

6

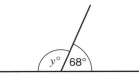

What is the size of the angle marked $y°$?

A   22°

B   112°

C   192°

D   122°

E   128°

7

What is the size of the angle marked $y°$?

A   180°

B   90°

C   45°

D $22\frac{1}{2}°$

E   60°

8

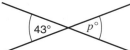

What is the size of the angle marked $p°$?

A   137°

B   57°

C   47°

D   43°

E   86°

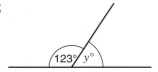

9

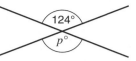

What is the size of the angle marked $p°$?

A 54°

B 56°

C 64°

D 62°

E 124°

10

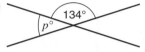

What is the size of the angle marked $p°$?

A 46°

B 56°

C 66°

D 62°

E 134°

11

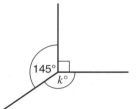

What is the size of the angle marked $k°$?

A 95°

B 65°

C 105°

D 125°

E 115°

12

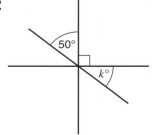

What is the size of the angle marked $k°$?

A 40°

B 50°

C 90°

D 45°

E 55°

13

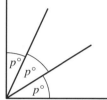

What is the size of the angle marked $p°$?

A 40°

B 50°

C 60°

D 30°

E 90°

14

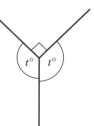

What is the size of the angle marked $t°$?

A 90°

B 45°

C 135°

D 145°

E 120°

8 Fractions and decimals

8.1 What is a fraction?

1

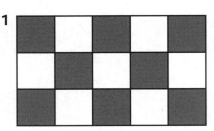

The fraction shaded is

A $\frac{1}{2}$

B $\frac{8}{7}$

C $\frac{7}{8}$

D $\frac{7}{15}$

E $\frac{8}{15}$

2 A bowl of fruit has 6 apples, 3 oranges and 5 bananas.
What fraction of the fruit are bananas?

A $\frac{5}{15}$

B $\frac{1}{3}$

C $\frac{5}{14}$

D $\frac{5}{9}$

E $\frac{9}{14}$

3

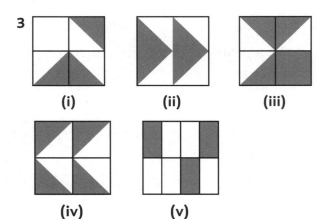

Which of the tiles are $\frac{3}{8}$ shaded?

A (i) and (v)

B (i)

C (i), (iii) and (v)

D (ii) and (iv)

E (v)

4 One of the tiles has a different fraction shaded. Which one?

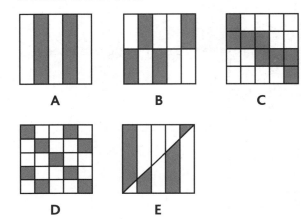

5 A bag contains coloured discs. 4 are red, 7 are blue, 3 are green and 6 are yellow. What fraction of the discs are blue?

A $\frac{7}{13}$

B $\frac{7}{20}$

C $\frac{13}{20}$

D $\frac{1}{4}$

E $\frac{7}{21}$

These diagrams are for questions **6** and **7**.

A   **B**   **C**

D   **E**

6 Which shape is half shaded?

7 How many shapes are more than half shaded?

   A 0

   B 1

   C 2

   D 3

   E 4

8 Which of these is the biggest fraction?

   A $\frac{1}{3}$

   B $\frac{1}{4}$

   C $\frac{1}{5}$

   D $\frac{1}{8}$

   E $\frac{1}{10}$

8.2 Equivalent fractions

1 If $\frac{24}{30} = \frac{x}{80}$, what is the value of x?

   A 72

   B 64

   C 65

   D 60

   E 56

2 If $\frac{32}{40} = \frac{x}{215}$, what is the value of x?

   A 192

   B 170

   C 172

   D 160

   E 176

3 If $\frac{18}{y} = \frac{27}{36}$, what is the value of y?

   A 21

   B 54

   C 30

   D 27

   E 24

4 If $\frac{70}{y} = \frac{2}{3}$, what is the value of y?

   A 105

   B 210

   C 72

   D 140

   E 120

5 What is the value of $\frac{84}{192}$?

   A $\frac{14}{31}$

   B $\frac{28}{63}$

   C $\frac{42}{94}$

   D $\frac{126}{288}$

   E $\frac{7}{16}$

6 What is the value of $\frac{100}{125}$?

   A $\frac{3}{4}$

   B $\frac{5}{6}$

   C $\frac{4}{5}$

   D $\frac{75}{100}$

   E $\frac{50}{75}$

7 Which fractions are equivalent to $\frac{2}{5}$?

(i) $\frac{6}{15}$ (ii) $\frac{12}{20}$ (iii) $\frac{10}{25}$ (iv) $\frac{46}{115}$ (v) $\frac{4}{10}$

A all of them

B all except (ii)

C all except (ii) and (iv)

D only (i) and (v)

E only (v)

8.3 Simplifying fractions

1 $\frac{18}{30}$ in its simplest form is

A $\frac{3}{5}$

B $\frac{9}{15}$

C $\frac{6}{9}$

D $\frac{2}{3}$

E $\frac{6}{10}$

2 $\frac{27}{36}$ in its simplest form is

A $\frac{3}{5}$

B $\frac{5}{6}$

C $\frac{9}{12}$

D $\frac{3}{4}$

E $\frac{2}{3}$

3 $\frac{42}{48}$ in its simplest form is

A $\frac{5}{6}$

B $\frac{6}{7}$

C $\frac{21}{24}$

D $\frac{14}{16}$

E $\frac{7}{8}$

4 Which fraction is not a simplification of $\frac{48}{72}$?

A $\frac{8}{12}$

B $\frac{16}{24}$

C $\frac{24}{28}$

D $\frac{2}{3}$

E $\frac{12}{18}$

5 Which fraction is a simplification of $\frac{108}{192}$?

A $\frac{54}{94}$

B $\frac{52}{96}$

C $\frac{36}{64}$

D $\frac{9}{18}$

E $\frac{27}{46}$

6 Which fractions are simplifications of $\frac{100}{150}$?

(i) $\frac{2}{3}$ (ii) $\frac{10}{15}$ (iii) $\frac{75}{125}$ (iv) $\frac{300}{450}$ (v) $\frac{4}{6}$

A all of them

B all of them except (iii)

C all except (iii) and (iv)

D only (i)

E only (i) and (v)

8.4 Ordering fractions

1 When $\frac{3}{5}, \frac{8}{15}, \frac{17}{30}$ are written in order, starting with the smallest, the order is

A $\frac{17}{30}, \frac{8}{15}, \frac{3}{5}$

B $\frac{3}{5}, \frac{8}{15}, \frac{17}{30}$

C $\frac{17}{30}, \frac{3}{5}, \frac{8}{15}$

D $\frac{8}{15}, \frac{3}{5}, \frac{17}{30}$

E $\frac{8}{15}, \frac{17}{30}, \frac{3}{5}$

2 Put $\frac{5}{6}, \frac{19}{24}, \frac{24}{30}$ in order of size, starting with the smallest.

   A $\frac{24}{30}, \frac{19}{24}, \frac{5}{6}$

   B $\frac{5}{6}, \frac{19}{24}, \frac{24}{30}$

   C $\frac{19}{24}, \frac{24}{30}, \frac{5}{6}$

   D $\frac{19}{24}, \frac{5}{6}, \frac{24}{30}$

   E $\frac{24}{30}, \frac{5}{6}, \frac{19}{24}$

3 Put $\frac{16}{20}, \frac{69}{85}, \frac{63}{80}$ in order of size, starting with the smallest.

   A $\frac{69}{85}, \frac{63}{80}, \frac{16}{20}$

   B $\frac{16}{20}, \frac{63}{80}, \frac{69}{85}$

   C $\frac{63}{80}, \frac{16}{20}, \frac{69}{85}$

   D $\frac{63}{80}, \frac{69}{85}, \frac{16}{20}$

   E $\frac{16}{20}, \frac{69}{85}, \frac{63}{80}$

4 Which fraction is smaller than $\frac{3}{8}$?

   A $\frac{7}{16}$

   B $\frac{8}{24}$

   C $\frac{27}{72}$

   D $\frac{19}{48}$

   E $\frac{16}{40}$

5 Which fraction is larger than $\frac{8}{15}$?

   A $\frac{24}{45}$

   B $\frac{16}{29}$

   C $\frac{31}{60}$

   D $\frac{40}{76}$

   E $\frac{16}{30}$

6 Which fraction is bigger than $\frac{7}{8}$?

   A $\frac{36}{40}$

   B $\frac{13}{16}$

   C $\frac{41}{48}$

   D $\frac{69}{80}$

   E $\frac{20}{24}$

7 Which fraction is smaller than $\frac{5}{7}$?

   A $\frac{51}{70}$

   B $\frac{36}{49}$

   C $\frac{21}{28}$

   D $\frac{37}{56}$

   E $\frac{16}{21}$

8.5 Improper fractions and mixed numbers

1 Which of the following has the same value as $3\frac{7}{9}$?

   A $\frac{37}{9}$

   B $\frac{34}{9}$

   C $\frac{21}{9}$

   D $\frac{66}{9}$

   E $\frac{10}{9}$

2 Which of the following has the same value as $2\frac{1}{3}$?

   A $\frac{7}{3}$

   B $\frac{5}{3}$

   C $\frac{21}{3}$

   D $\frac{8}{3}$

   E $\frac{12}{3}$

3 Which of the following has the same value as $4\frac{3}{5}$?

A $\frac{17}{5}$

B $\frac{19}{5}$

C $\frac{34}{5}$

D $\frac{23}{5}$

E $\frac{43}{5}$

4 What is $\frac{13}{5}$ written as a mixed number?

A $1\frac{3}{5}$

B $2\frac{1}{5}$

C $2\frac{3}{5}$

D $\frac{3}{5}$

E $1\frac{8}{5}$

5 What is $\frac{24}{9}$ when written as a mixed number?

A $2\frac{4}{9}$

B $1\frac{15}{9}$

C $\frac{8}{3}$

D $2\frac{1}{9}$

E $2\frac{2}{3}$

8.6 Reading and writing decimals

1

The reading on this scale is

A 2.3

B 2.6

C 2.7

D 2.8

E 2.9

2

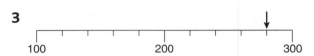

The reading on this scale is

A 5.2

B 4.7

C 5.5

D 5.4

E 5.7

3

The reading on this scale is

A 275

B 270

C 280

D 290

E 230

4

The reading on this scale is

A −3.4

B −3.8

C −4.1

D −4.2

E −3.2

8.7 Understanding place value

1 The value of the 7 in 32 700 is

A 7 thousands

B 7 hundredths

C 7 tens

D 7 hundreds

E 7 thousandths

2 The value of 3 in 2.730 is

  A 3 hundredths

  B 3 hundreds

  C 3 tens

  D 3 tenths

  E 3 thousandths

3 The value of the 3 in 27.31 is

  A 3 hundredths

  B 3 tenths

  C 3 tens

  D 3 hundreds

  E 3 thousandths

For questions **4** to **7** it is given that
$3.26 \times 0.017 = 0.05542$

4 What is the value of 326×0.017?

  A 0.5542

  B 5.542

  C 55.42

  D 0.05542

  E 55.42

5 What is the value of 0.326×17?

  A 0.5542

  B 0.05542

  C 55.42

  D 5.542

  E 55.42

6 What is the value of $5542 \div 170$?

  A 3.26

  B 0.326

  C 32.6

  D 326

  E 3260

7 What is the value of $55.42 \div 32.6$?

  A 17

  B 170

  C 0.17

  D 0.017

  E 1.7

8.8 Ordering decimals

1 3.343   3.44   3.34   3.434   3.33

When these numbers are written in order of size, the middle number is

  A 3.44

  B 3.34

  C 3.343

  D 3.434

  E 3.33

2 6.703   6.71   6.723   6.8   6.716

When these numbers are written in order of size, starting with the smallest, then the fourth number will be

  A 6.716

  B 6.703

  C 6.71

  D 6.723

  E 6.8

3 0.06   0.051   0.0493   0.0503   0.04856

Which of the following has these numbers in order of increasing size?

  A 0.0485 0.0493 0.051 0.0503 0.06

  B 0.0485 0.0493 0.06 0.051 0.0503

  C 0.0485 0.0493 0.0503 0.051 0.06

  D 0.06 0.051 0.0485 0.0493 0.0503

  E 0.051 0.0485 0.0493 0.0503 0.06

4 0.07   0.023   0.065   0.0663   0.06063

The largest of these numbers is

A   0.07

B   0.023

C   0.065

D   0.0663

E   0.06063

5 11.123   11.321   11.231   11.024   11.031

When written in order, the middle number will be

A   11.024

B   11.031

C   11.231

D   11.321

E   11.123

6 2.0807   2.0709   2.0805   2.071   2.0713

When written in order, starting with the smallest, the second number will be

A   2.0805

B   2.071

C   2.0807

D   2.0709

E   2.0713

8.9 Converting decimals to fractions

1 0.4 as a fraction in its simplest form is

A $\frac{4}{10}$

B $\frac{40}{100}$

C $\frac{1}{4}$

D $\frac{2}{5}$

E $\frac{1}{2}$

2 0.06 written as a fraction in its simplest form is

A $\frac{6}{100}$

B $\frac{6}{10}$

C $\frac{3}{50}$

D $\frac{1}{6}$

E $\frac{1}{60}$

3 0.023 written as a fraction is

A $\frac{10}{23}$

B $\frac{23}{1000}$

C $\frac{23}{100}$

D $\frac{23}{10}$

E $\frac{100}{23}$

4 0.45 written as a fraction in its simplest form is

A $\frac{45}{100}$

B $\frac{45}{1000}$

C $\frac{4}{9}$

D $\frac{18}{40}$

E $\frac{9}{20}$

5 0.032 written as a fraction in its simplest form is

A $\frac{4}{125}$

B $\frac{8}{25}$

C $\frac{8}{250}$

D $\frac{32}{1000}$

E $\frac{32}{100}$

6 0.28 written as a fraction in its simplest form is

A $\frac{28}{1000}$

B $\frac{14}{50}$

C $\frac{28}{100}$

D $\frac{7}{250}$

E $\frac{7}{25}$

8.10 Converting fractions to decimals

1 What is $\frac{3}{8}$ written as a decimal?

A 0.37

B 0.375

C 0.325

D 0.4

E 0.5

2 What is $\frac{5}{9}$ written as a decimal?

A 0.5

B 0.55

C 0.555

D $0.\dot{5}$

E 0.6

3 What is $\frac{1}{11}$ written as a decimal?

A $0.\dot{0}\dot{9}$

B $0.0\dot{9}$

C 0.091

D 0.1

E 0.11

4 What is $\frac{5}{8}$ written as a decimal?

A 0.6

B 0.65

C 0.625

D 0.675

E 0.5

5 What is $\frac{24}{100}$ written as a decimal?

A 0.2

B 0.25

C 0.3

D 0.024

E 0.24

6 What is $\frac{13}{25}$ written as a decimal?

A 0.13

B 0.26

C 0.48

D 0.52

E 0.5

7 What is $\frac{3}{1000}$ written as a decimal?

A 0.03

B 0.3

C 0.0003

D 0.003

E 0.00333

8 What is $\frac{8}{500}$ written as a decimal?

A 0.016

B 0.0016

C 0.16

D 0.004

E 0.0625

9 Directed numbers

9.1 What is a directed number?

1 Which of the following has these numbers in order of size, starting with the smallest?

1	2	−4	−3	−7

A 1   2   −3   −4   −7

B −3   −4   −7   1   2

C −7   −4   −3   1   2

D −7   −3   −4   1   2

E −7   −4   1   2   −3

2 Which of the following has these numbers in order of size, starting with the smallest?

0	−2	4	−5	−3

A −5   −3   −2   0   4

B −4   0   −2   −3   −5

C 0   −2   −3   4   −5

D −5   −2   −3   0   4

E 0   −5   −3   −2   4

3 Work out the value of −3 − 2

A +5

B −1

C +6

D −5

E −6

4 Work out the value of −5 + 2

A −3

B −7

C −10

D 10

E +3

5 Work out the value of +8 − 16

A $-\frac{1}{2}$

B $\frac{1}{2}$

C −8

D 8

E −24

6 Which of the following has these temperatures in order of size, starting with the highest?

6°C	−2°C	−5°C	3°C	−8°C

A 6°C   3°C   −2°C   −5°C   −8°C

B 6°C   3°C   −8°C   −5°C   −2°C

C −8°C   6°C   −5°C   3°C   −2°C

D −8°C   −5°C   −2°C   3°C   6°C

E 6°C   3°C   −8°C   −2°C   −5°C

9.2 Addition and subtraction of directed numbers

1 Work out (−7) − (−2)

A −5

B 5

C $3\frac{1}{2}$

D 9

E −9

2 Work out (+36) − (−19)

A −17

B 17

C 45

D −55

E 55

3 Work out $(-15) + (+3)$

   A -18

   B 18

   C -12

   D 12

   E -5

4 Work out $(+23) + (-2)$

   A -21

   B 21

   C 25

   D -25

   E -46

5 Work out $(+8) + (-2)$

   A 10

   B -10

   C 6

   D -6

   E -4

6 Work out $(-21) - (-7)$

   A 28

   B -28

   C 3

   D -14

   E 14

7 Work out $(-18) - (-24)$

   A 42

   B -42

   C 0.75

   D 6

   E -6

8 Work out $(+6) - (+8)$

   A 2

   B -2

   C 14

   D -14

   E $-\frac{3}{4}$

9.3 Multiplication and division of directed numbers

1 Work out $(-16) \div (-4)$

   A $\frac{1}{4}$

   B $-\frac{1}{4}$

   C -20

   D 4

   E -4

2 Here are three statements

  (i) $-6 \times -3 = 18$

  (ii) $4 \times -2 = -8$

  (iii) $-5 \times -2 = -10$

  Which option describes these statements?

   A All are correct

   B (ii) and (iii) are correct

   C (i) and (ii) are correct

   D Only (ii) is correct

   E Only (iii) is correct

3 Work out $(+25) \div (-5)$

   A -5

   B 5

   C $-\frac{1}{5}$

   D $\frac{1}{5}$

   E 20

4 Work out $\left(+\frac{1}{4}\right) \div (-4)$

  A   0

  B $-\frac{1}{16}$

  C $\frac{1}{16}$

  D   1

  E -1

5 Work out $(-12) \times \left(-\frac{1}{3}\right)$

  A $\frac{1}{36}$

  B $-\frac{1}{36}$

  C   36

  D -4

  E   4

6 Work out $\left(+\frac{1}{4}\right) \div \left(-\frac{1}{2}\right)$

  A -2

  B   2

  C $-\frac{1}{8}$

  D $\frac{1}{2}$

  E $-\frac{1}{2}$

7 Here are three statements
  (i) $(-21) \div (+7) = -3$
  (ii) $\left(-\frac{1}{2}\right) \div (+2) = -1$
  (iii) $(-14) \div (-21) = \frac{2}{3}$

Which option describes these three statements?

  A   (i) and (ii) are true

  B   (i) and (iii) are true

  C   (ii) and (iii) are true

  D   All three are true

  E   Only (i) is true

8 Work out $-10 \times -\frac{1}{5}$

  A -2

  B -50

  C   2

  D   50

  E   10.2

10 Decimals

10.1 Rounding decimals

1 What is 354.7 when rounded to the nearest number?

   A 400

   B 350

   C 355

   D 354

   E 354.7

2 What is £5.67 when rounded to the nearest pound?

   A £5.60

   B £5.70

   C £5.67

   D £5.00

   E £6.00

3 What is 29.47 m when rounded to the nearest metre?

   A 29.5

   B 30

   C 29.4

   D 29

   E 29.5

4 What is 2.199 g when rounded to the nearest kg?

   A 2.2

   B 2

   C 2.1

   D 3

   E 2.19

5 What is 65.493 when rounded to the nearest whole number?

   A 65

   B 65.4

   C 65.5

   D 66

   E 70

6 What is 74.55 cm when rounded to the nearest cm?

   A 74

   B 75

   C 74.6

   D 74.5

   E 70

7 What is 482.901 when rounded to the nearest whole number?

   A 480

   B 482

   C 483

   D 482.9

   E 482.90

10.2 Estimating

1 Which is the best estimate for the value of 4.9×2.1?

   A 10

   B 100

   C 980

   D 98

   E 49

2 Which is the best estimate for the value of 19.6 × 32.4?

   A 280

   B 57

   C 900

   D 600

   E 120

3 Which is the best estimate for the value of 203 × 79?

   A 160

   B 16 000

   C 3200

   D 14 000

   E 140

4 Which is the best estimate for the value of 802 ÷ 3.9?

   A 800

   B 260

   C 200

   D 80

   E 20

5 Which is the best estimate for the value of 574 ÷ 3.1?

   A 19

   B 200

   C 570

   D 600

   E 20

6 Which is the best estimate for the value of 69.2 × 81.5?

   A 4800

   B 560

   C 480

   D 150

   E 5600

7 Which is the best estimate for the value of 6819 ÷ 71.2?

   A 700

   B 600

   C 100

   D 70

   E 60

10.3 Adding and subtracting decimals

1 What is 2.67 + 10.8?

   A 3.75

   B 13.47

   C 12.75

   D 1347

   E 12.15

2 What is 83.47 − 28.74?

   A 65.33

   B 50

   C 54.73

   D 6533

   E 5473

3 What is 18 + 23.45 + 1.872?

A   43.322

B   42.35

C   25.502

D   25.5

E   42

4 What is 22 − 8.47?

A   8.23

B   14.53

C   14.63

D   30.47

E   13.53

5 Jon buys a jacket for £63.49 and a pair of trousers for £28.99.
What is the total amount he paid?

A   £81.38

B   £92.48

C   £92.38

D   £92.98

E   £82.48

6 Emma buys 30 metres of internet cable. She uses 8.45 metres to connect a computer.
What length of cable is left?

A   21 m

B   38.45 m

C   22.65 m

D   21.55 m

E   21.65 m

7 Chris buys a sandwich for £2.95 and a drink for £1.28. He pays with a £10 note.
How much money should he have left?

A   £4.23

B   £5.77

C   £6.87

D   £6.13

E   £14.23

10.4 Multiplying decimals

1 What is 5.14 × 8?

A   41.12

B   408.32

C   4.112

D   4112

E   40.8

2 What is 0.456 × 1000?

A   0.0456

B   0.456

C   4.56

D   45.6

E   456

3 What is 1.07 × 100?

A   0.0107

B   0.107

C   1.07

D   10.7

E   107

4 What is 2.61 × 0.03?

- **A** 7.83
- **B** 0.783
- **C** 0.0783
- **D** 78.3
- **E** 783

5 What is 0.054 × 0.37?

- **A** 0.54
- **B** 0.019 98
- **C** 0.1998
- **D** 0.000 54
- **E** 0.001 998

6 A memory stick costs £1.35.
What would be the total cost of buying
1000 of these memory sticks?

- **A** £1.35
- **B** £13.50
- **C** £135
- **D** £1350
- **E** £13 500

7 £1 is worth $2.20. How much is £0.85
worth?

- **A** $3.05
- **B** $1.87
- **C** $2.86
- **D** $18.70
- **E** $2.03

10.5 Dividing decimals

1 What is 34.8 ÷ 2?

- **A** 16.4
- **B** 17.4
- **C** 174
- **D** 0.174
- **E** 1.64

2 What is 4.24 ÷ 100?

- **A** 424
- **B** 42.4
- **C** 4.24
- **D** 0.424
- **E** 0.0424

3 What is 0.76 ÷ 1000?

- **A** 0.000 76
- **B** 0.0076
- **C** 0.076
- **D** 0.76
- **E** 7.6

4 What is 16.26 ÷ 0.03?

- **A** 5.42
- **B** 0.542
- **C** 542
- **D** 0.0542
- **E** 54.2

5 What is 0.5096 ÷ 0.008?

- **A** 0.000 006 37
- **B** 0.637
- **C** 0.0637
- **D** 63.7
- **E** 6.37

6 A tank contains 69 litres of water. The water is to be used to fill bottles which each contain 0.3 litres of water. How many bottles can be filled?

A 207

B 23

C 230

D 20

E 66

7 Metal washers weigh 0.04 kg each. A box contains 1 kg of washers. How many washers are there in the box?

A 25

B 250

C 2500

D 25 000

E 250 000

10.6 Further estimates

1 Which is the best estimate for the value of 38 books at £6.95 each?

A £200

B £280

C £180

D £300

E £190

2 Which is the best estimate for the value of 82 maths kits at £4.15 each?

A £320

B £380

C £32

D £300

E £400

3 Which is the best estimate for the value of 5954×0.049?

A 5000

B 200

C 500

D 300

E 2000

4 Which is the best estimate for the value of $784.3 \div 0.079$?

A 7000

B 1000

C 70

D 10 000

E 8000

5 Which is the best estimate for the value of $\dfrac{42.4}{1.9 \times 3.78}$?

A 40

B 5

C 4

D 50

E 10

6 Which is the best estimate for the value of $\dfrac{886 \times 40.2}{8.79}$?

A 300

B 400

C 40

D 3000

E 4000

7 Which is the best estimate for the value of $\dfrac{218.3 \times 37.8}{79.2}$?

A 640

B 90

C 100

D 1000

E 200

10.7 Rounding to decimal places

1 What is the number 2.364 rounded to 2 decimal places?

A 2.35

B 2.3

C 2.36

D 2.364

E 2

2 What is the number 15.678 rounded to 2 decimal places?

A 15

B 15.7

C 15.67

D 16

E 15.68

3 What is the number 0.575 rounded to 2 decimal places?

A 0.6

B 0.58

C 0.57

D 0.575

E 0.5

4 What is the number 76.394 rounded to 1 decimal place?

A 76.3

B 80

C 76.4

D 76.39

E 76

5 What is the number 0.006 65 rounded to 3 decimal places?

A 0.007

B 0.006 65

C 0.006

D 0.0066

E 0.0067

6 What is the number 8.377 rounded to 2 decimal places?

A 8.37

B 8.377

C 8.3

D 8.38

E 8.4

7 What is the number 0.0555 rounded to 3 decimal places?

A 0.555

B 0.056

C 0.55

D 0.06

E 0.556

10.8 Rounding to significant figures

1 What is the number 96.121 rounded to 1 significant figure?

A 100

B 96.1

C 96

D 97

E 96.12

2 What is the number 71.335 rounded to 1 significant figure?

A 71.3

B 71

C 70

D 71.33

E 71.34

3 What is the number 0.0175 rounded to 1 significant figure?

A 0.01

B 0.02

C 0.017

D 0.018

E 1

4 What is the number 1.0926 rounded to 1 significant figure?

A 1.1

B 1.09

C 10

D 1.093

E 1

5 What is the number 0.00555 rounded to 1 significant figure?

A 0.005

B 1

C 0.006

D 0.0056

E 5

6 What is the number 255.78 rounded to 1 significant figure?

A 3

B 256

C 255.7

D 300

E 255.8

7 What is the number 306.43 rounded to 1 significant figure?

A 306.4

B 300

C 400

D 310

E 306

10.9 Problems with decimals

1 What is the total weight of 24 parcels each weighing 34.8 grams?

A 208.8 g

B 835.2 g

C 765.6 g

D 722.2 g

E 1461.6 g

2 How many lengths of material, each 0.15 metres, can be cut from a 3 metre length of material?

   A 0.45

   B 15

   C 2

   D 2.85

   E 20

3 The takings at a small shop over a 5-day period are £145.68, £109.87, £99.56, £175.31 and £122.61. What is the total?

   A £553.15

   B £530.42

   C £653.03

   D £477.72

   E £553.47

4 A car driver calculates that she can travel 13.5 miles for every litre of petrol. How many miles can she travel on 38 litres?

   A 513

   B 148.5

   C 2.8

   D 24.5

   E 342

5 Bob has to pay £37.67 for his train ticket, and £5.28 for a taxi. How much change will he have out of £50?

   A £42.95

   B £8.05

   C £8.15

   D £7.05

   E £12.33

6 Some curtains need 0.95 metres of fabric. What is the total length of fabric needed for 14 curtains?

   A 14.7 m

   B 140 m

   C 13.3 m

   D 133 m

   E 147 m

7 Mary is paid £8.50 each week to deliver a free newspaper. How much is she paid in a year? (1 year = 52 weeks)

   A £44.20

   B £424

   C £442

   D £458

   E £452

11 Algebra

11.1 Using letters to represent numbers

1 Two apples are added to a bowl containing x apples.
How many apples are now in the bowl?

A $x + 2$

B $2x$

C $x \div 2$

D x^2

E $2 - x$

2 Three boxes each contain s sweets.
The total number of sweets is

A $\dfrac{3}{s}$

B $\dfrac{s}{3}$

C $3s$

D $3 + s$

E s^3

3 William buys 5 pencils. Each pencil costs p pence.
How much do these 5 pencils cost?

A $\dfrac{5}{p}$

B $\dfrac{p}{5}$

C p^5

D $5 + p$

E $5p$

4 Mary has a collection of x postcards.
She sells 10 of them at a collectors fair.
How many postcards does she have now?

A $10 - x$

B $x - 10$

C $\dfrac{x}{10}$

D $\dfrac{10}{x}$

E $x + 10$

5 Alan thinks of a number. He multiplies it by 3 and adds 2 to the result.
If Alan thought of y, what is the number Alan ends up with?

A $y + 6$

B $3y^2$

C $3y + 2$

D $3y - 2$

E $3y \times 2$

11.2 Expressions and terms

1 How many terms are there in this expression?

$$3x + 2y + wz$$

A 6

B 1

C 5

D 4

E 3

2 How many terms are there in this expression?

$$2x^2y + 3xz$$

A 2

B 1

C 3

D 4

E 5

3 How many terms are there in this expression?

$$p(2x + 3y)$$

A 6

B 5

C 3

D 2

E 1

4 Tulips cost £3 a bunch. Daffodils cost £2 a bunch.
Which of the following is an expression, in £, for the cost of x bunches of tulips and y bunches of daffodils?

A $2x \times 3y$

B $5(x + y)$

C $3x + 2y$

D $2x + 3y$

E $6xy$

5 x sweets are shared equally between y children. There are no sweets left over.
How many sweets does each child get?

A $\dfrac{y}{x}$

B $\dfrac{x}{y}$

C $x - y$

D $y - x$

E xy

6 m matches are needed to fill a box.
x boxes of matches are filled from a pile of matches with 5 left over.
How many matches were in the pile?

A $5x + m$

B $5m + x$

C $m + x + 5$

D $mx + 5$

E $5mx$

7 There are n people on a bus.
The bus stops and p people get on and q people get off.
How many people are now on the bus?

A $n + p - q$

B $n + q - p$

C $\dfrac{np}{q}$

D $\dfrac{nq}{p}$

E $(n - p)q$

8 $2\pi r(r + h)$ is an expression for working out the surface area of a cylinder where r is the radius and h is the height, π is a constant.
How many variables are there in the expression?

A 1

B 4

C 3

D 2

E 5

9 $6x^2y$ is an expression for working out a volume. x and y are lengths.
How many variables are there in the expression?

A 3

B 4

C 2

D 0

E 1

12 Perimeter and area of 2-D shapes

12.1 Perimeter

1 This rectangle is drawn on a centimetre grid.

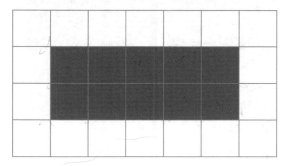

What is the perimeter of the rectangle?

A   10 cm

B   12 cm

C   14 cm

D   11 cm

E   7 cm

2 Here is a shape drawn on a centimetre grid.

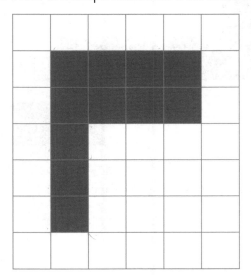

What is the perimeter of the shape?

A   11 cm

B   18 cm

C   16 cm

D   17 cm

E   19 cm

3 What is the perimeter of this rectangle?

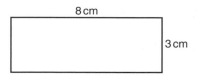

A   22 cm

B   24 cm

C   11 cm

D   19 cm

E   14 cm

4 What is the perimeter of this triangle?

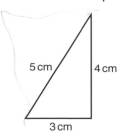

A   10 cm

B   7 cm

C   12 cm

D   8 cm

E   9 cm

5 What is the perimeter of this shape?

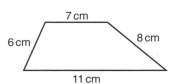

A   17 cm

B   15 cm

C   24 cm

D   32 cm

E   26 cm

6 This is an isosceles triangle.

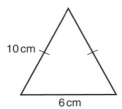

What is its perimeter?

A 16 cm

B 22 cm

C 20 cm

D 26 cm

E 60 cm

7 What is the perimeter of this shape?

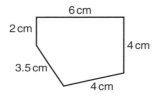

A 18.5 cm

B 20 cm

C 20.5 cm

D 12 cm

E 19.5 cm

12.2 Area

1 This rectangle is drawn on a centimetre grid.

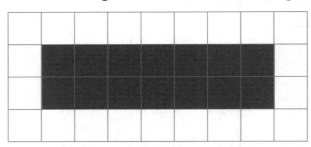

What is the area of the rectangle?

A 14 cm

B 14 cm²

C 12 m²

D 16 cm²

E 36 cm

2 Here is a shape drawn on a centimetre grid.

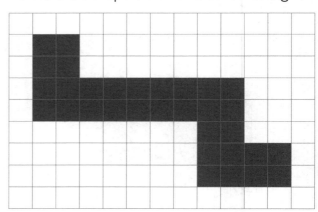

What is the area of the shape?

A 26 cm²

B 32 cm²

C 24 cm²

D 36 cm²

E 77 cm²

3 Here is a shape drawn on a centimetre grid.

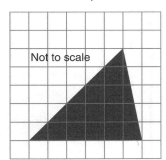

Work out an estimate for the area of this shape.

A 30 cm²

B 10 cm²

C 15 cm²

D 12 cm²

E 18 cm²

4 Here is a shape drawn on a centimetre grid.

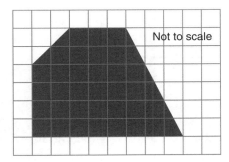

Work out an estimate for the area of this shape.

A 40 cm²

B 37 cm²

C 45 cm²

D 29 cm²

E 30 cm²

5 Here is a shape drawn on a centimetre grid.

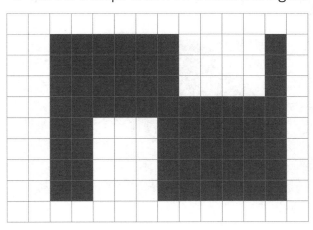

The area of the shape is

A 64 cm²

B 66 cm²

C 86 cm²

D 63 cm²

E 60 cm²

6 Here is a shape drawn on a centimetre grid.

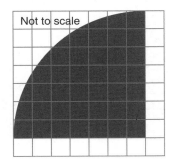

Work out an estimate for the area of this shape.

A 36 cm²

B 30 cm²

C 20 cm²

D 28 cm²

E 26 cm²

7 Here is a shape drawn on a centimetre grid.

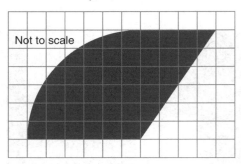

Work out an estimate for the area of this shape.

A 52 cm²

B 34 cm²

C 44 cm²

D 48 cm²

E 38 cm²

12.3 Areas of rectangles, squares, triangles and parallelograms

1

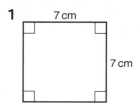

7 cm

7 cm

The area of this shape is

A 49 cm

B 7 cm²

C 48 cm²

D 49 cm²

E 14 cm

2 Here is a rectangle.

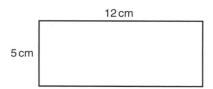

12 cm

5 cm

The area of the rectangle is

A 60 cm²

B 5 cm²

C 34 cm²

D 72 cm²

E 48 cm²

3

6 cm

8 cm

The area of this triangle is

A 48 cm²

B 28 cm²

C 24 cm²

D 12 cm²

E 14 cm²

4

4 cm

What is the area of this parallelogram?

A 32 cm²

B 24 cm²

C 12 cm²

D 24 cm²

E 30 cm²

5 A rectangle has a length of 5 cm and an area of 40 cm².
What is the width of the rectangle?

A 48 cm

B 8 cm

C 15 cm

D 6 cm

E 10 cm

6 A triangle has an area of 36 cm² and a height of 9 cm.
Work out the length of the base of the triangle.

A 45 cm

B 18 cm

C 8 cm

D 4 cm

E 27 cm

12.4 Problems involving areas

1 Work out the area of this shape.

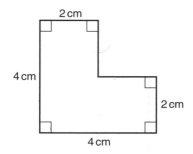

A 16 cm²

B 12 cm

C 14 cm²

D 10 cm²

E 12 cm²

2 Work out the area of this shape.

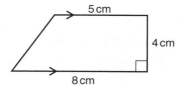

A 26 cm²

B 20 cm²

C 17 cm²

D 40 cm²

E 160 cm²

3

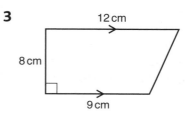

The area of this trapezium is

A 168 cm²

B 84 cm²

C 72 cm²

D 96 cm²

E 108 cm²

4 A wall measures 4 m by 2 m.
The wall is to be covered with tiles measuring 50 cm by 50 cm.
How many tiles are needed to cover the wall completely?

A 16

B 8

C 32

D 24

E 64

13 Sequences

13.1 Sequences

1 This sequence of patterns is made from crosses. How many crosses are there in the next pattern?

A 15

B 13

C 14

D 11

E 12

2 This sequence of patterns is made from sticks. How many sticks are there in the next pattern?

A 19

B 23

C 21

D 20

E 22

3 Here is a sequence of numbers:
5, 8, 11, 14, 17, …
What is the next number in this sequence?

A 21

B 18

C 22

D 19

E 20

4 Here is a sequence of numbers:
7, 12, 17, 22, …
What is the next number in this sequence?

A 26

B 29

C 28

D 27

E 25

5 Here is a sequence of numbers:
3, 7, 11, 15, …
What is the 10th term in this sequence?

A 39

B 10

C 41

D 19

E 40

6 Here is a sequence of numbers:
2, 8, 14, 20, …
What is the 10th term in this sequence?

A 10

B 26

C 50

D 60

E 56

13.2 Input and output machines

1 What is the inverse of $+5 \times 3$?

A -3×5

B $-5 \div 3$

C $\times 3 + 5$

D $\div 3 - 5$

E $\times 3 - 5$

2 What is the inverse of ÷2 − 4?

A +4 × 2

B −4 ÷ 2

C +4 ÷ 2

D ×2 + 4

E +2 × 4

3 When the input is 6, what is the output for this machine?

A 30

B 18

C 22

D 19

E 2

4 When the input is 18, what is the output for this machine?

A 3

B 66

C 1

D 2

E 10

5 When the output is 8, what is the input for this machine?

A 20

B 0

C 24

D 8

E 4

6 When the output is 8, what is the input for this machine?

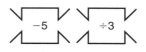

A 39

B 2

C 16

D 1

E 29

13.3 Finding an expression for the *n*th term of an arithmetic sequence

1 Here are the first five terms of an arithmetic sequence.

  5, 9, 13, 17, 21

What is the expression, in terms of *n*, for the *n*th term of this sequence?

A *n*

B 25

C 5*n*

D 4*n* + 1

E $\frac{n}{4}$

2 Here are the first five terms of an arithmetic sequence.

  6, 9, 12, 15, 18

What is the expression, in terms of *n*, for the *n*th term of this sequence?

A 6*n*

B 3*n*

C $\frac{n}{3}$

D 21

E 3*n* + 3

3 Here are the first five terms of an arithmetic sequence.

5, 7, 9, 11, 13

What is the expression, in terms of n, for the nth term of this sequence?

A $2n$

B $\dfrac{n}{5}$

C $2n + 3$

D $3n$

E $5n$

4 Here are the first five terms of an arithmetic sequence.

3, 7, 11, 15, 19

What is the expression, in terms of n, for the nth term of this sequence?

A n

B $3n$

C $4n$

D $4n - 1$

E $\dfrac{n}{3}$

5 Here are the first five terms of an arithmetic sequence.

6, 8, 10, 12, 14

What is the expression, in terms of n, for the nth term of this sequence?

A $2n + 4$

B $6n$

C $2n$

D $4n$

E $\dfrac{n}{6}$

6 Here are the first five terms of an arithmetic sequence.

1, 4, 7, 10, 13

What is the expression, in terms of n, for the nth term of this sequence?

A $2n$

B $3n - 2$

C n

D $3n$

E 16

14 Angles 2

14.1 Triangles

1 What is the size of the angle marked x in this triangle?

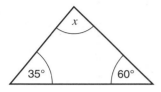

A 95°

B 35°

C 75°

D 85°

E 60°

2 What is the size of the angle marked y in this triangle?

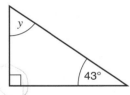

A 157°

B 47°

C 57°

D 90°

E 43°

3 What is the size of the angle marked r in this triangle?

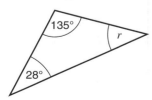

A 28°

B 37°

C 17°

D 12°

E 135°

4 What is the size of the angle marked p in this triangle?

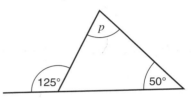

A 50°

B 55°

C 75°

D 125°

E 80°

5 What is the size of the angle marked t in this triangle?

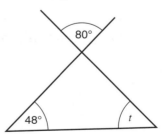

A 48°

B 84°

C 20°

D 80°

E 52°

14.2 Equilateral and isosceles triangles

1 What is the size of the angle marked x in this triangle?

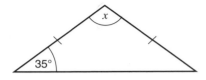

- **A** 35°
- **B** 130°
- **C** 110°
- **D** 70°
- **E** 55°

2 What is the size of the angle marked z in this triangle?

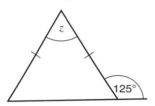

- **A** 70°
- **B** 125°
- **C** 55°
- **D** 110°
- **E** $62\frac{1}{2}°$

3 What is the size of the angle marked g in this triangle?

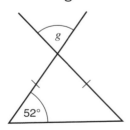

- **A** 110°
- **B** 52°
- **C** 38°
- **D** 76°
- **E** 128°

4 What is the size of the angle marked h in this triangle?

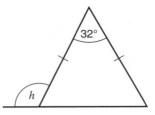

- **A** 32°
- **B** 106°
- **C** 64°
- **D** 148°
- **E** 74°

5 What is the size of the angle marked i in this triangle?

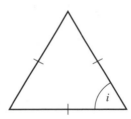

- **A** 30°
- **B** 25°
- **C** 33°
- **D** 60°
- **E** 65°

15 Graphs

15.1 Coordinates in the first quadrant

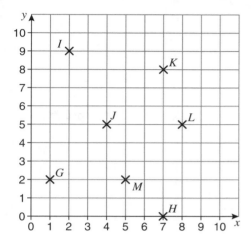

1 What are the coordinates of the point *G*?

   A (2, 1)

   B (−1, −2)

   C (1, 2)

   D (−2, −1)

   E (2, 2)

2 What are the coordinates of the point *H*?

   A (0, −7)

   B (0, 7)

   C (−7, 0)

   D (7, 7)

   E (7, 0)

3 What are the coordinates of the point *I*?

   A (−2, 9)

   B (2, 9)

   C (2, −9)

   D (9, 2)

   E (2, 2)

4 What are the coordinates of the point *J*?

   A (4, 5)

   B (−4, 5)

   C (5, 4)

   D (5, 5)

   E (4, 4)

5 What are the coordinates of the point *K*?

   A (8, 8)

   B (8, 7)

   C (7, 8)

   D (−7, −8)

   E (−7, 8)

6 What are the coordinates of the point *L*?

   A (5, 8)

   B (8, 8)

   C (−8, −5)

   D (8, 5)

   E (−8, 5)

7 What are the coordinates of the point *M*?

   A (2, 5)

   B (5, 2)

   C (−5, −2)

   D (−5, 2)

   E (5, −2)

15.2 Coordinates in all four quadrants

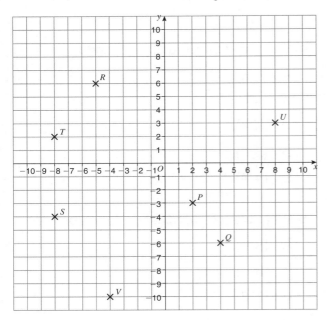

1 What are the coordinates of the point P?

   A $(-2, 3)$

   B $(2, -3)$

   C $(-2, -3)$

   D $(2, 3)$

   E $(-3, 3)$

2 What are the coordinates of the point Q?

   A $(-4, 6)$

   B $(-6, 4)$

   C $(4, -6)$

   D $(6, -4)$

   E $(-4, -6)$

3 What are the coordinates of the point R?

   A $(-5, 6)$

   B $(6, -5)$

   C $(5, -6)$

   D $(-5, -6)$

   E $(-6, -5)$

4 What are the coordinates of the point S?

   A $(-4, -8)$

   B $(-8, 4)$

   C $(4, -8)$

   D $(-8, -4)$

   E $(-4, -8)$

5 What are the coordinates of the point T?

   A $(2, -8)$

   B $(8, -2)$

   C $(-8, 2)$

   D $(-2, -8)$

   E $(-8, -2)$

6 What are the coordinates of the point U?

   A $(3, 8)$

   B $(-8, 3)$

   C $(3, -8)$

   D $(-8, -3)$

   E $(8, 3)$

7 What are the coordinates of the point V?

   A $(-10, -4)$

   B $(-10, 4)$

   C $(4, -10)$

   D $(-4, 10)$

   E $(-4, -10)$

15.3 Finding the coordinates of the midpoint of a line

1

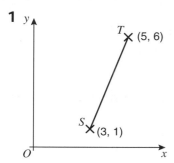

The coordinates of the midpoint of the line *ST* are

A $(3\frac{1}{2}, 2)$

B $(2, 4\frac{1}{2})$

C $(4, 3\frac{1}{2})$

D $(2\frac{1}{2}, 3\frac{1}{2})$

E $(3\frac{1}{2}, 4)$

2

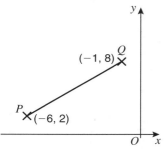

The coordinates of the midpoint of the line *PQ* are

A $(-2.5, 3)$

B $(-3.5, 5)$

C $(-3.5, 4)$

D $(5, -3.5)$

E $(2.5, -3)$

3

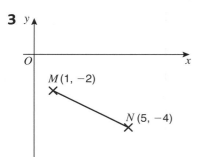

The coordinates of the midpoint of the line *MN* are

A $(3, -3)$

B $(-3, 3)$

C $(3, 3)$

D $(-3, -3)$

E $(2, -1)$

4 What are the coordinates of the midpoint of the line joining the points (1, 4) and (3, 10)?

A $(2, 6)$

B $(-2, 7)$

C $(2, -7)$

D $(2, 7)$

E $(7, 2)$

5 What are the coordinates of the midpoint of the line joining the points $(-3, 5)$ and $(-5, -5)$?

A $(0, -4)$

B $(-4, 0)$

C $(-1, -5)$

D $(1, 5)$

E $(-4, -5)$

6 The point (4, 5) is the midpoint of the line *XY*. The coordinates of *X* are (2, 1). What are the coordinates of *Y*?

A $(9, 6)$

B $(2, 3)$

C $(6, 9)$

D $(3, 3\frac{1}{2})$

E $(6, 6)$

17 Measure

17.1 Reading scales

1 What is the reading on these scales?

A 1.7 kg

B 1.3 kg

C 1.6 kg

D 1.4 kg

E 1.5 kg

2 What is the reading on this ruler?

A 3.1

B 3.01

C 3.0

D 3.2

E 3.05

3 Look at this number line.

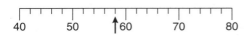

What value is shown by the arrow on the number line?

A 54

B 58

C 59

D 57.5

E 56

4 Look at this number line.

What value is shown by the arrow on the number line?

A 1.23

B 1.25

C 1.26

D 1.24

E 1.28

5 What is the reading on this speedometer?

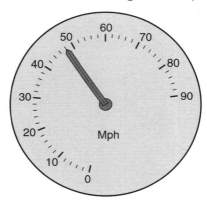

A 44

B 48

C 46

D 49

E 47

6 What is the number marked by the arrow on this number line

A 62.04

B 62.2

C 62.02

D 62.5

E 62.4

17.2 Time

1 What is 3 20 pm in 24-hour clock time?

  A 17 20

  B 03 20

  C 13 20

  D 15 20

  E 14 20

2 What is 5 45 am in 24-hour clock time?

  A 5 45

  B 05 45

  C 17 45

  D 50 45

  E 19 45

3 What is 10 past 2 in the morning written in 12-hour clock time?

  A 10.2 am

  B 2.10 am

  C 2.10 pm

  D 10 20 am

  E 2.10

4 What is a quarter to 11 in the evening in 24-hour clock time?

  A 2.3 15

  B 11 45

  C 11 15

  D 23 45

  E 22 45

5 What is 6 hours written in minutes?

  A 360

  B 300

  C 420

  D 72

  E 720

6 How many hours are there in 3 days?

  A 36

  B 180

  C 84

  D 72

  E 70

7 A train leaves Euston at 13 05 and arrives in Manchester at 15 35.
How long does the train journey take?

  A 1 hour 30 minutes

  B 2 hours 40 minutes

  C 2 hours 35 minutes

  D 2 hours 30 minutes

  E 1 hour 30 minutes

8 How many seconds are there in $6\frac{1}{2}$ minutes?

  A 78

  B 390

  C 330

  D 76

  E 360

17.3 Units

1 Here is a man stood next to a building. They are both drawn to the same scale.

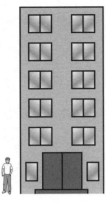

Estimate the height of the building.

A 10 m

B 4 m

C 8 m

D 5 m

E 12 m

2 What unit is sensible to use to measure the distance between London and Brighton?

A Feet

B Inches

C Yards

D Metres

E Miles

3 What unit is sensible to use to measure the weight of a sack of potatoes?

A Tonnes

B Grams

C Kilograms

D Pints

E Litres

4 The diagram shows a dog tied to a lamppost. They are drawn to the same scale. The dog is 30 cm tall.

Estimate the height of the lamppost.

A 4.5 m

B 3.0 m

C 350 cm

D 6.0 m

E 550 cm

17.4 Converting between metric units

1 What is 6 cm in millimetres?

A 600

B 60

C 0.6

D 6.6

E 6000

2 What is 4000 m in kilometres?

    A   40

    B   4

    C   400

    D   40 000

    E   0.4

3 What is 9000 kg in tonnes?

    A   900

    B   0.9

    C   90

    D   9

    E   90 000

4 What is 4 litres in millilitres?

    A   40

    B   400

    C   4000

    D   40 000

    E   0.4

20 Three-dimensional shapes

20.8 Coordinates in three dimensions

1

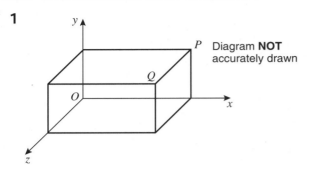

The point Q has coordinates (6, 2, 4).
What are the coordinates of the point P?

A (6, 2, 0)

B (6, 0, 4)

C (0, 2, 4)

D (6, 4, 0)

E (4, 2, 6)

2

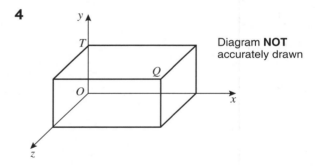

The point Q has coordinates (6, 2, 4).
What are the coordinates of the point R?

A (6, 2, 0)

B (6, 0, 4)

C (0, 2, 4)

D (6, 4, 0)

E (4, 2, 6)

3

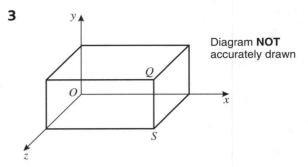

The point Q has coordinates (6, 2, 4).
The coordinates of the point S are?

A (6, 2, 0)

B (6, 0, 4)

C (0, 2, 4)

D (6, 4, 0)

E (4, 2, 6)

4

The point Q has coordinates (6, 2, 4).
The coordinates of the point T are?

A (6, 2, 0)

B (6, 0, 4)

C (0, 2, 4)

D (6, 4, 0)

E (0, 2, 0)

5

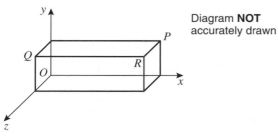

Diagram **NOT** accurately drawn

The point P has coordinates $(7, 2, 0)$.
The point Q has coordinates $(0, 2, 3)$.
What are the coordinates of the point R?

A $(7, 2, 0)$

B $(7, 2, 3)$

C $(7, 0, 3)$

D $(7, 0, 0)$

E $(0, 0, 3)$

6

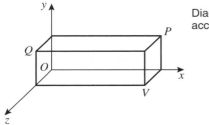

Diagram **NOT** accurately drawn

The point P has coordinates $(7, 2, 0)$.
The point Q has coordinates $(0, 2, 3)$.
What are the coordinates of the point V?

A $(7, 2, 0)$

B $(7, 2, 3)$

C $(7, 0, 3)$

D $(7, 0, 0)$

E $(0, 0, 3)$

7

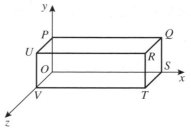

Diagram **NOT** accurately drawn

R has coordinates $(8, 3, 2)$.
Which point has coordinates $(8, 0, 2)$?

A Q

B T

C U

D V

E P

8

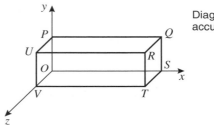

Diagram **NOT** accurately drawn

R has coordinates $(8, 3, 2)$.
Which point has coordinates $(8, 3, 0)$?

A Q

B T

C U

D V

E P

22 Estimating and accuracy

22.1 Rounding

1 What is 8.8 to the nearest integer?

  A 8

  B 9

  C 8.5

  D 10

  E 1

2 The number 8765 rounded to the nearest 100 is

  A 8700

  B 88

  C 87

  D 8800

  E 8000

3 The number 7.562 to 1 significant figure is

  A 8

  B 7

  C 7.6

  D 7.5

  E 10

4 Work out an estimate for 33×28

  A 2500

  B 600

  C 900

  D 1200

  E 800

5 What is a sensible estimate for $4024 \div 215$?

  A $4000 \div 250$

  B $4000 \div 200$

  C $5000 \div 250$

  D $10\,000 \div 100$

  E $5000 \div 200$

6 Work out an estimate for $\dfrac{3.8 \times 5.2}{9.7}$

  A 10

  B 3

  C 5

  D 4

  E 2

7 The number 952.71 to 1 significant figure is

  A 950

  B 1000

  C 900

  D 952.7

  E 953

22.2 Solving problems using approximations

1 The cost of a bus fare is £1.56.
What is the approximate cost of 8 tickets?

  A £20

  B £15

  C £12

  D £16

  E £10

2 A book weighs 357 g.
What is the approximate weight of
22 books?

  A   700 g

  B   9000 g

  C   10 000 g

  D   8000 g

  E   6000 g

3 Mary earns £5.95 an hour.
She works for 38 hours.
What is a good estimate for her total
earnings?

  A   £240

  B   £200

  C   £300

  D   £150

  E   £180

4 Work out an estimate for $\dfrac{46.1 \times 33.2}{5.3}$

  A   150

  B   300

  C   320

  D   400

  E   240

5 Work out an estimate for $\dfrac{72.6 + 25}{12.1 + 1.3}$

  A   100

  B   32

  C   10

  D   25

  E   50

6 A lawn measures 76 m by 113 m.
Estimate the area of the lawn.

  A   150 000 m^2

  B   5000 m^2

  C   10 000 m^2

  D   8000 m^2

  E   500 m^2

23 Two-dimensional shapes

23.2 Triangles

1 Which one of these triangles is a right-angled triangle?

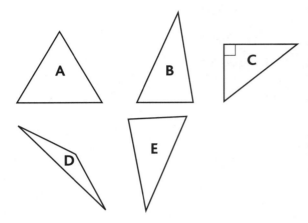

2 Which one of these triangles is an isosceles triangle?

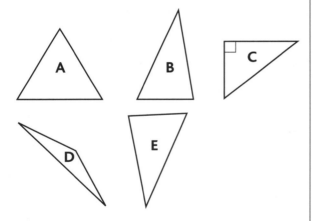

3 Which one of these triangles is an equilateral triangle?

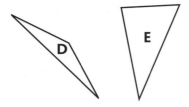

4 In which one of these triangles are all the angles exactly 60°?

  A Equilateral

  B Isosceles

  C Right-angled

  D Scalene

  E Obtuse

5 Which one of these triangles always has exactly two sides the same length?

  A Equilateral

  B Isosceles

  C Right-angled

  D Scalene

  E Obtuse

6 Which one of these triangles always has exactly one angle that is 90°?

  A Equilateral

  B Isosceles

  C Right-angled

  D Scalene

  E Obtuse

23.3 Symmetry of quadrilaterals

1 Which one of these quadrilaterals has exactly one pair of parallel sides?

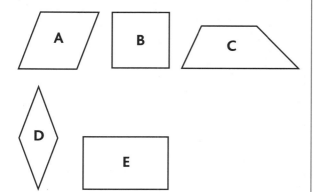

2 Which one of these quadrilaterals has exactly four sides of equal length?

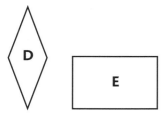

3 Which one of these quadrilaterals has only opposite sides equal in length and four right-angles?

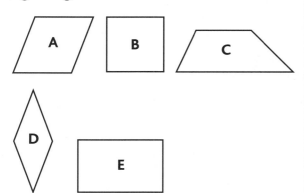

4 Which one of these shapes is a quadrilateral that always has only two pairs of adjacent sides equal in length?

  A Triangle

  B Parallelogram

  C Trapezium

  D Kite

  E Rectangle

5 Which one of these shapes has opposite sides that are parallel and equal in length, but no right angles?

  A Square

  B Parallelogram

  C Trapezium

  D Kite

  E Rectangle

6 Which one of these shapes has opposite sides that are parallel, all sides equal in length, but no right angles?

  A Rhombus

  B Parallelogram

  C Trapezium

  D Kite

  E Rectangle

Practice Paper 1
Answer ALL TWENTY FIVE questions
You must NOT use a calculator

1 Here is a shaded shape on a centimetre grid.

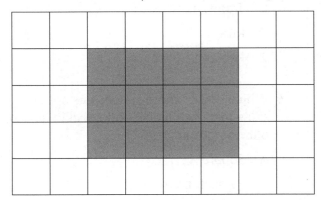

What is the area of the shaded shape?

14 cm²	7 cm²	10 cm²	9 cm²	12 cm²
A	B	C	D	E

2 Here is a list of numbers.

  2   3   4   5   6

Which of these numbers is a factor of 35?

2	3	4	5	6
A	B	C	D	E

3 During one week a shopping precinct had 13 367 visitors.
  What is the number 13 367 rounded to the nearest hundred?

13 300	13 000	14 000	100	13 400
A	B	C	D	E

4 Here is a list of decimal numbers.

    6.4   6.41   6.39   6.389   6.3

Tom is going to write these numbers in order of size.
He writes down the largest number.
Which number should he write down next?

6.4	6.41	6.39	6.389	6.3
A	**B**	**C**	**D**	**E**

5 Here is a sequence of patterns made from sticks.

Pattern 1	Pattern 2	Pattern 3	Pattern 4
8 sticks	15 sticks	22 sticks	

What is the number of sticks needed for Pattern 4?

7	29	30	26	36
A	**B**	**C**	**D**	**E**

6 Write the number 12 030 in words.

Twelve hundred and three

A

One thousand two hundred and thirty

B

Twelve hundred and thirty

C

Twelve thousand and thirty

D

Twelve thousand and three

E

7 Here are five angles.
Which marked angle is a right-angle?

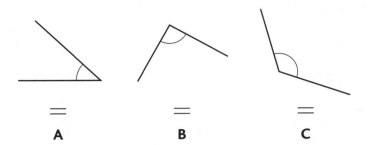
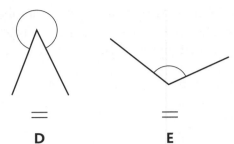

=	=	=	=	=
A	**B**	**C**	**D**	**E**

8 Here is a part of a bus timetable.

Acre Road	08 15	08 45	09 15
Bulls Head	08 22	08 52	09 22
Craddock Park	08 31	09 01	09 30
Duck Street	08 42	09 11	09 39

A bus leaves Acre Road at 08 45.
At what time should the bus arrive at Craddock Park?

08 45	08 52	09 01	09 15	09 30
=	=	=	=	=
A	**B**	**C**	**D**	**E**

9 Here are the first four numbers in a sequence.

    10   16   22   28

What is the next number in the sequence?

31	32	40	34	35
=	=	=	=	=
A	**B**	**C**	**D**	**E**

10 Here is a rectangle.

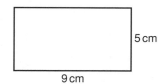

Diagram NOT
accurately drawn

5 cm

9 cm

What is the perimeter of the rectangle?

45 cm	14 cm	106 cm	28 cm	24.5 cm
A	B	C	D	E

11

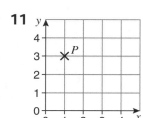

What are the coordinates of point P?

$(1, -3)$	$(-3, 1)$	$(3, 1)$	$(-1, 3)$	$(1, 3)$
A	B	C	D	E

12 A television programme starts at 2.40 pm and lasts for 1 hour and 35 minutes.
At what time does the programme finish?

3 15 pm	4 15 pm	2 55 pm	3 75 pm	4 05 pm
A	B	C	D	E

13

Diagram NOT accurately drawn

What is the size of the angle marked x?

160°	80°	100°	120°	200°
=	=	=	=	=
A	**B**	**C**	**D**	**E**

14 Which of these fractions is equivalent to $\frac{4}{5}$?

$\frac{6}{7}$	$\frac{10}{12}$	$\frac{16}{20}$	$\frac{15}{20}$	$\frac{7}{10}$
=	=	=	=	=
A	**B**	**C**	**D**	**E**

15 What is the number 43.827 correct to 1 significant figure?

40	43	43.8	43.9	45
=	=	=	=	=
A	**B**	**C**	**D**	**E**

16

Diagram NOT accurately drawn

In triangle ABC, angle $A = 60°$, angle $B = 50°$.
What is the size of angle x?

50°	100°	110°	70°	90°
=	=	=	=	=
A	**B**	**C**	**D**	**E**

17 What is -7 added to 4?

$+3$	-3	-7	-11	11
$=$	$=$	$=$	$=$	$=$
A	**B**	**C**	**D**	**E**

18 Which one of the following shapes has exactly four sides the same length?

Rhombus	Rectangle	Kite	Trapezium	Parallelogram
$=$	$=$	$=$	$=$	$=$
A	**B**	**C**	**D**	**E**

19

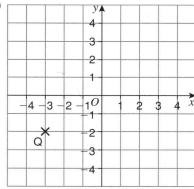

What are the coordinates of point Q?

$(3, 2)$	$(-3, 2)$	$(-2, -3)$	$(-2, 3)$	$(-3, -2)$
$=$	$=$	$=$	$=$	$=$
A	**B**	**C**	**D**	**E**

20 It costs Sean £26 for each weekly train ticket he buys.
Sean buys n tickets during a school term.
Find an expression, in terms of n, for the cost, in pounds, of buying the tickets.

n	$n + 26$	$2600n$	$26n$	$\dfrac{n}{26}$
$=$	$=$	$=$	$=$	$=$
A	**B**	**C**	**D**	**E**

21 Find the lowest common multiple (LCM) of 15 and 50.

3	5	15	150	750
=	=	=	=	=
A	**B**	**C**	**D**	**E**

22 Katy buys 26 mathematical instrument sets for £5.65 each.
What is the total cost?

£350.30	£45.20	£146.90	£39.58	£158.20
=	=	=	=	=
A	**B**	**C**	**D**	**E**

23 A square board has a side of length 1 metre.
A hole 30 cm by 20 cm is cut out of it.

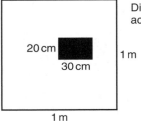

Diagram **NOT**
accurately drawn

20 cm
30 cm
1 m
1 m

What is the area, in cm², of card left?

599	9400	40	400	5000
=	=	=	=	=
A	**B**	**C**	**D**	**E**

24

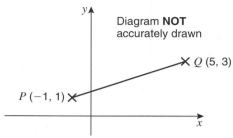

Diagram **NOT** accurately drawn

Q (5, 3)

P (−1, 1)

The coordinates of the midpoint of the line PQ are

(4, 4)	(4, 2)	(3, 2)	(3, 1)	(2, 2)
=	=	=	=	=
A	**B**	**C**	**D**	**E**

25 Here are the first five terms of an arithmetic sequence..

10   18   26   34   42

Find an expression, in terms of n, for the nth term of the sequence.

$n − 8$	$8n − 2$	$n + 8$	$8n + 2$	$8n$
A	**B**	**C**	**D**	**E**

TOTAL FOR PAPER: 25 MARKS

Practice Paper 2
Answer ALL TWENTY FIVE questions
You must NOT use a calculator

1 What is 15 942 when rounded to the nearest 1000?

16	16 000	15	15 000	15 900
=	=	=	=	=
A	**B**	**C**	**D**	**E**

2 Ted buys a pen for £1.85 and a pencil for 65p.
What is the total cost?

£2.40	£3.40	£3.50	£2.50	£2.45
=	=	=	=	=
A	**B**	**C**	**D**	**E**

3

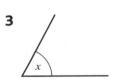

What type of angle is marked x?

Acute angle	Obtuse angle	Right angle	Reflex angle	x angle
=	=	=	=	=
A	**B**	**C**	**D**	**E**

4 Here is a shaded shape on a grid of centimetre squares.

What is the area of the shaded shape?

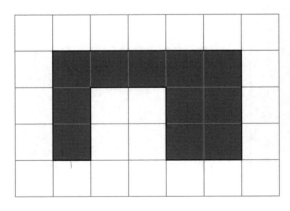

9 cm²	10 cm²	11 cm²	12 cm²	13 cm²
=	=	=	=	=
A	**B**	**C**	**D**	**E**

5 Here are the first four numbers in a sequence.

    4   10   16   22

The next number in the sequence is

30	29	27	28	34
=	=	=	=	=
A	**B**	**C**	**D**	**E**

6 The second odd number is 3.

What is the ninth odd number?

9	17	15	19	18
=	=	=	=	=
A	**B**	**C**	**D**	**E**

7 What is the value of the 7 in the number 3721?

70	7	700	7000	$\frac{7}{10}$
=	=	=	=	=
A	**B**	**C**	**D**	**E**

8 What number is shown by the arrow?

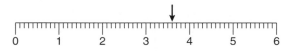

36	3.1	4.4	3.6	3.7
=	=	=	=	=
A	**B**	**C**	**D**	**E**

9 Which list of numbers is in order of size?

−5 −3 −1 7 2	7 2 −5 −3 −1	−1 −3 −5 2 7
=	=	=
A	**B**	**C**

−1 2 3 −5 7	−5 −3 −1 2 7
=	=
D	**E**

10 Here is a shaded shape on a grid of centimetre squares.

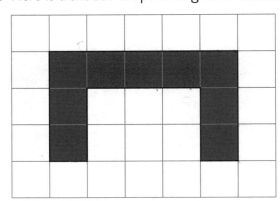

What is the perimeter of the shaded shape?

17 cm	18 cm	19 cm	20 cm	21 cm
=	=	=	=	=
A	**B**	**C**	**D**	**E**

11 Bags of crisps cost 35 pence each.
Rani buys b bags of crisps.

What is the expression, in terms of b, for the total cost?

b	$\dfrac{b}{35}$	$35b + 35$	$\dfrac{35}{b}$	$35b$
=	=	=	=	=
A	**B**	**C**	**D**	**E**

12

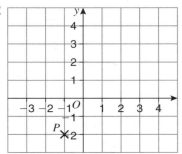

What are the coordinates of point P?

$(-2, 1)$	$(2, -1)$	$(-1, -2)$	$(-2, -1)$	$(2, 1)$
=	=	=	=	=
A	**B**	**C**	**D**	**E**

13 186 is divided by 14

What is the remainder?

10	4	3	2	18
=	=	=	=	=
A	**B**	**C**	**D**	**E**

14 2   4   5   6   9   15

Which two of the numbers above are square numbers?

4 and 9	5 and 6	9 and 15	5 and 9	2 and 5
=	=	=	=	=
A	**B**	**C**	**D**	**E**

15 Here is an isosceles triangle.

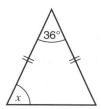

What is the size of the angle marked x?

36°	108°	144°	72°	54°
=	=	=	=	=
A	**B**	**C**	**D**	**E**

16 What is the area of this shaded shape?

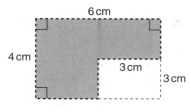

30 cm²	26 cm²	144 cm²	18 cm²	15 cm²
=	=	=	=	=
A	**B**	**C**	**D**	**E**

17 Apples cost a pence each.
Bananas cost b pence each.

Rachael buys 3 apples and 7 bananas.

What is the expression, in terms of x and y, for the total cost?

$3a + 7b$	$a + b$	$7a + 3b$	$10ab$	$10(a + b)$
A	B	C	D	E

18 What is the value of 325×23?

1745	3915	8700	3045	7475
A	B	C	D	E

19 Siobhan measured the length of a line as 45 mm.

What is this length in centimetres?

45 cm	450 cm	4500 cm	4.5 cm	0.45 cm
A	B	C	D	E

20 The nth term of a sequence is given by $5n - 3$

What is the 8th term of this sequence?

53	47	43	37	25
A	B	C	D	E

21 What is 0.25 when written as a fraction?

$\frac{2}{5}$	$\frac{1}{8}$	$\frac{1}{4}$	$\frac{5}{2}$	$\frac{1}{2}$
A	B	C	D	E